THE TRIWIZARD CUP

The Triwizard Tournament is on! But, wait a minute. Where's the winner's trophy? Use the stickers to conjure it.

As of this moment, the Triwizard Tournament has begun!

AGE LIMIT

Stick in the portraits to discover who drank an Ageing Potion to enter the Tournament. Psst! They have the fewest portraits here.

Mark the imposters with beard stickers.

CHAMPION SELECTION

The Goblet of Fire chooses who will compete in the Triwizard Tournament. Stick the chosen champions over the correct shapes.

FLEUR DELACOUR – The charming representative of the Beauxbatons school.

CEDRIC DIGGORY – The well-known and popular representative of Hogwarts.

VIKTOR KRUM – The representative of Durmstrang and a star Quidditch player.

HARRY POTTER – Wait, wait! His name should not have been put in the Goblet of Fire at all! Harry is too young to compete.

SPECIAL EDITION

The champions are featured in the *Daily Prophet*.
Stick in their photo, then mark six differences
between the photo and the large illustration.

Diggory

Vikto...

Harry Potter

A MAGIC BADGE

In a moment this magic badge will change beyond recognition! Place the stickers to complete the transformation.

Potter
STINKS

A BURNING SECRET

Harry already knows what the champions will face during the first task. Stick the fragments in the correct order to reveal the secret.

Oh, crikey!

FACE THE DRAGON

The first task is to retrieve a golden egg guarded by a dragon. Complete the tangle with stickers and pair each beast to each champion.

1 Swedish Short-Snout

3 Hungarian Horntail

2 Common Welsh Green

4 Chinese Fireball

TROUBLE!

The dragon is very close! Follow the colour sequence to help guide Harry. Mark the right way with stickers.

START

KEY:

FINISH

Use your stickers to make the egg become golden again.

AN EGG SURPRISE

The golden egg contained only ... a piercing screech! Complete the pictures with stickers. Then mark the two where everyone covers their ears.

What was that?

THE DANCE CHALLENGE

It's time for a dance lesson! Follow the clues and mark all the places on the dance floor where the dancers might slip.

CLUES

- The numbers indicate how many puddles should be around them.
- No two puddles should be placed next to each other.

THE KING OF THE DANCE FLOOR

Neville is practising dancing again! Stick in the missing spins, so that each set contains five different dance moves.

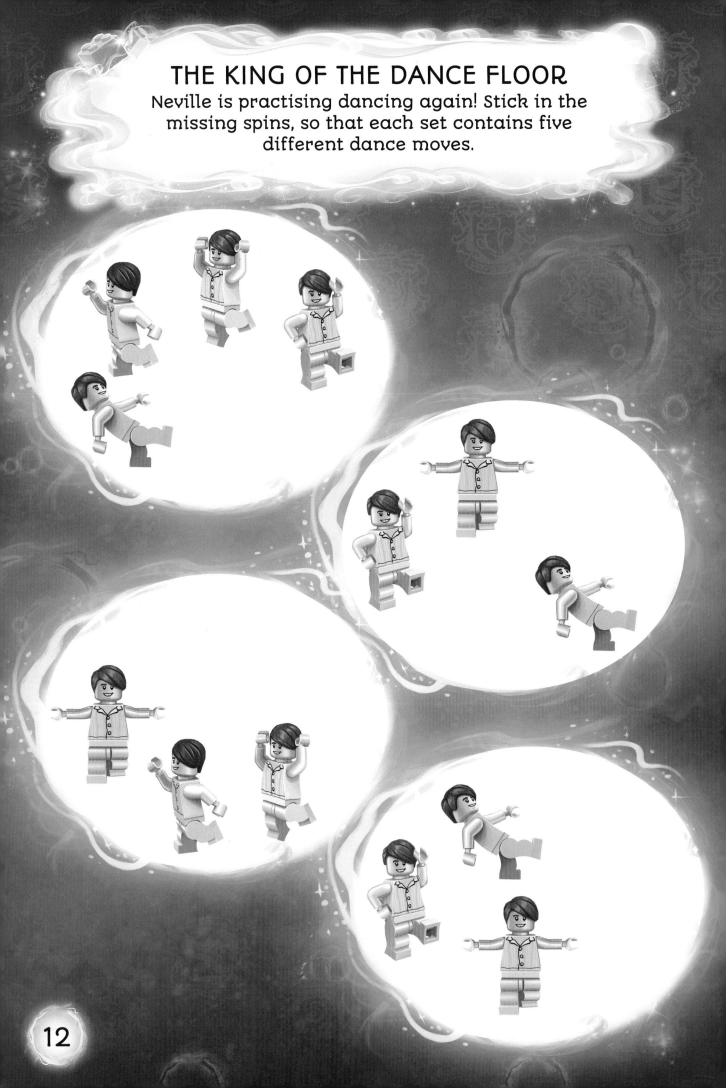

A TRUE IDOL

A crowd of fans keep following Viktor Krum. Use your stickers to make an escape path for him, so he can train in peace.

START

FINISH

CHIC AND STYLISH

Everyone looks spectacular at the Yule Ball. See for yourself and place the correct character stickers next to the outfit close-ups.

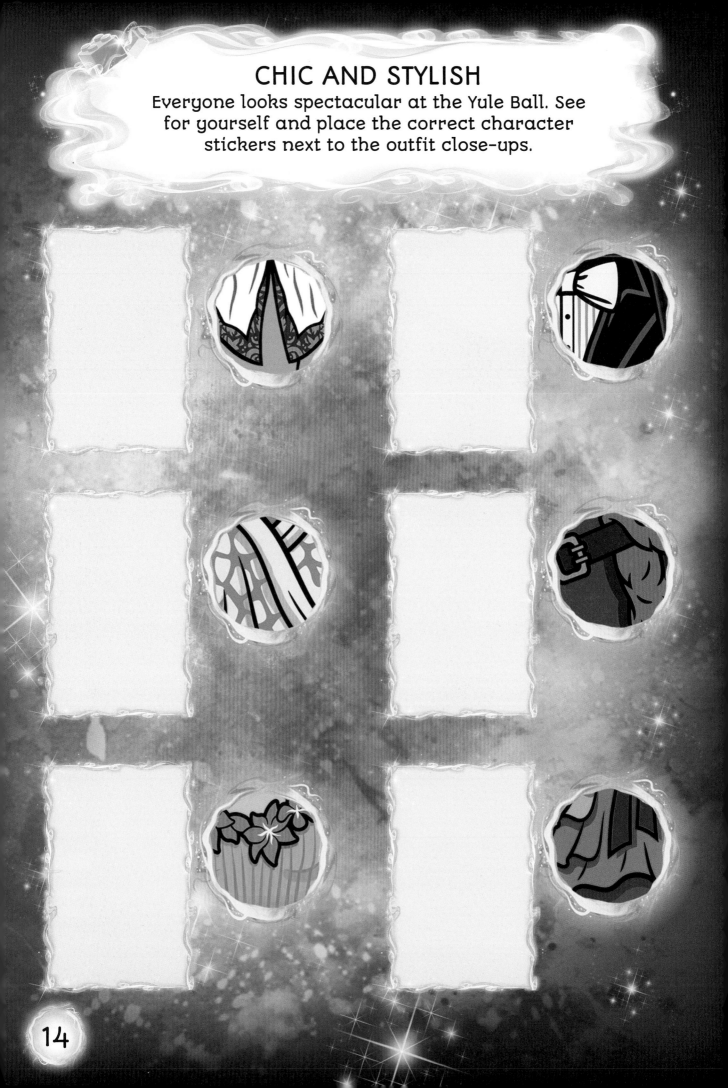

WIZARD STYLE

Ron is going to wear a traditional dress robe.
Use your stickers to create the mirror reflection
of Ron to see his outfit.

HAVING FUN?

Fill in the blank spaces with the correct stickers so that the layout of the bored faces matches the layout in the big grid.

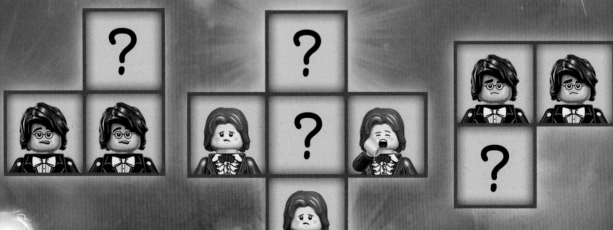

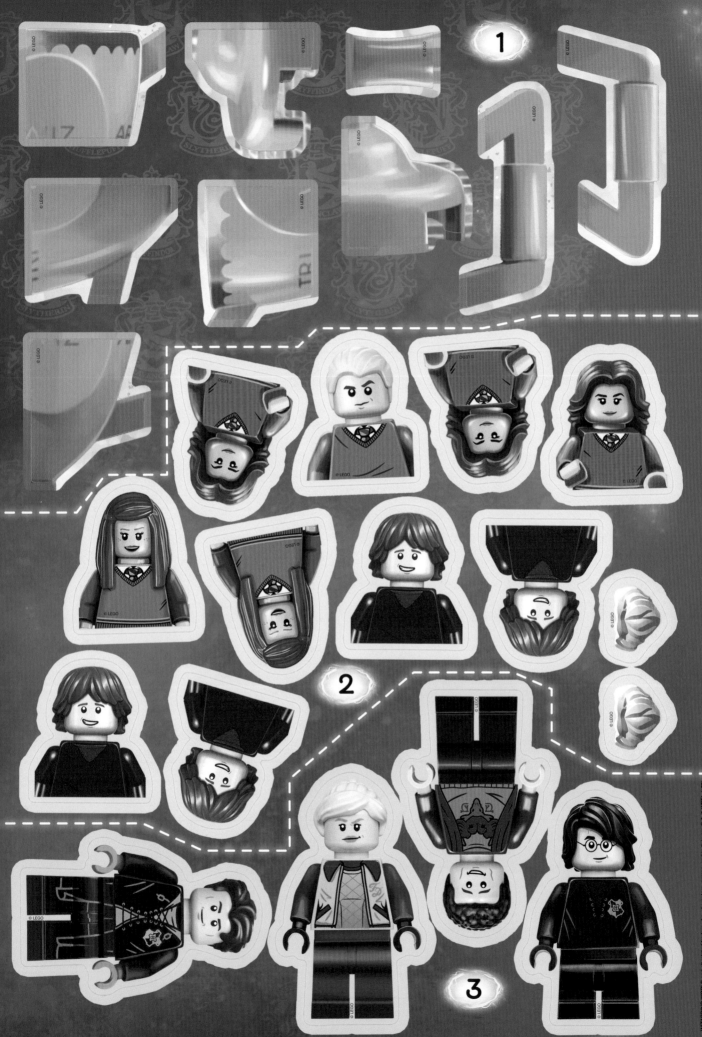

8-9

7

12

10

11

13

14

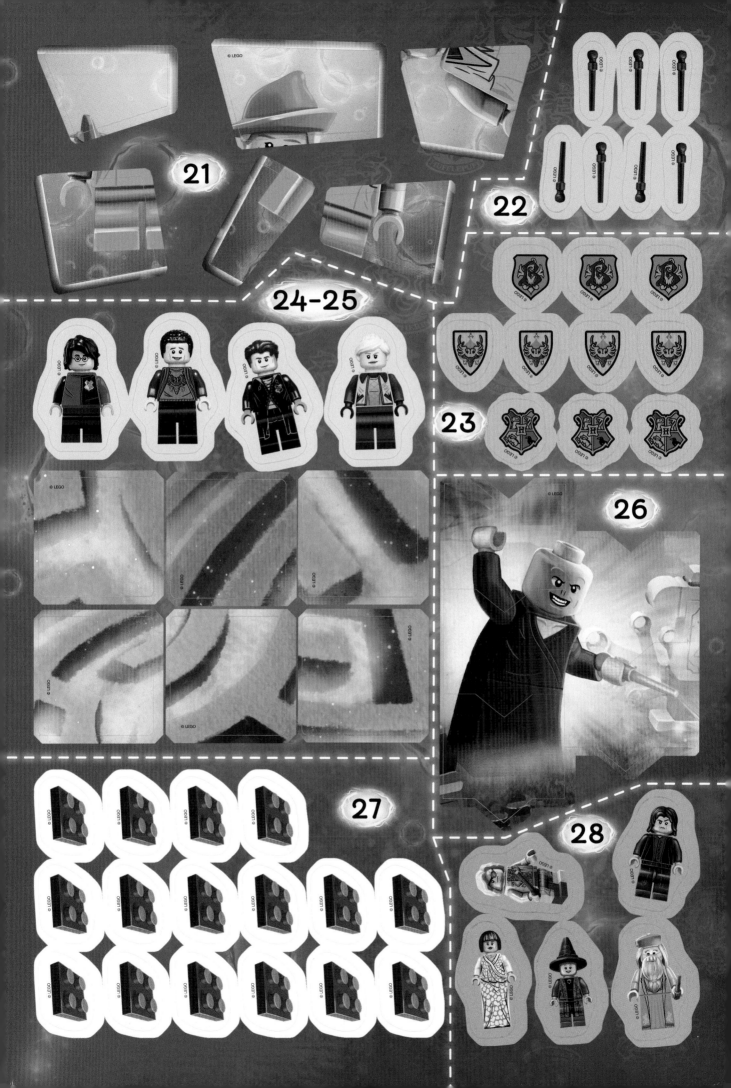

15

16

17

18

4

6

5

AN INCREDIBLE CREATURE

Harry and Cedric already know who they're going to face in the second task. Use your stickers to reveal the image.

UNDERWATER TRICKS

How will the champions breathe underwater?
Place the character stickers next to the spell
with the matching colour code.

BUBBLE-HEAD CHARM

TRANSFIGURATION

GILLYWEED

BUBBLE-HEAD CHARM

AN AMAZING TRANSFORMATION

A Grindylow, or maybe a merperson? Complete the empty spaces with stickers to find out what Viktor transfigures into.

TIME TASK

Decipher the pattern and stick in the correct clock stickers. The clock in the green circle shows when the second task will start.

You may begin at the sound of the cannon!

RESCUE MISSION

The competitors must save their friends trapped at the bottom of the lake. Use your stickers to help them see in the murky water.

THE RIGHT SPELL

Cover every second letter with stickers. The remaining letters will form a spell to make Harry jump out of the lake.

A G S I C O E

R N U D C I A O

ANSWER:

....

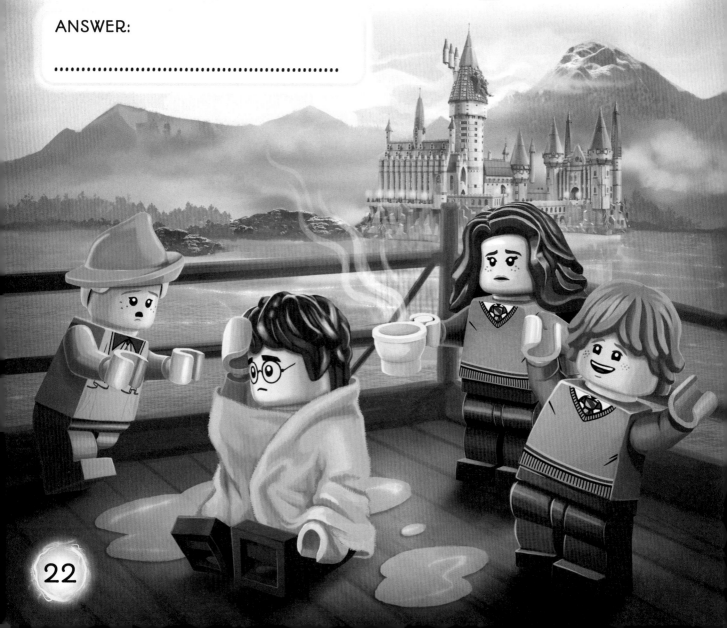

IN THE LEAD

Use stickers to make sure neighbouring bricks contain the same school crests. The numbers show which school is in which place in the tournament.

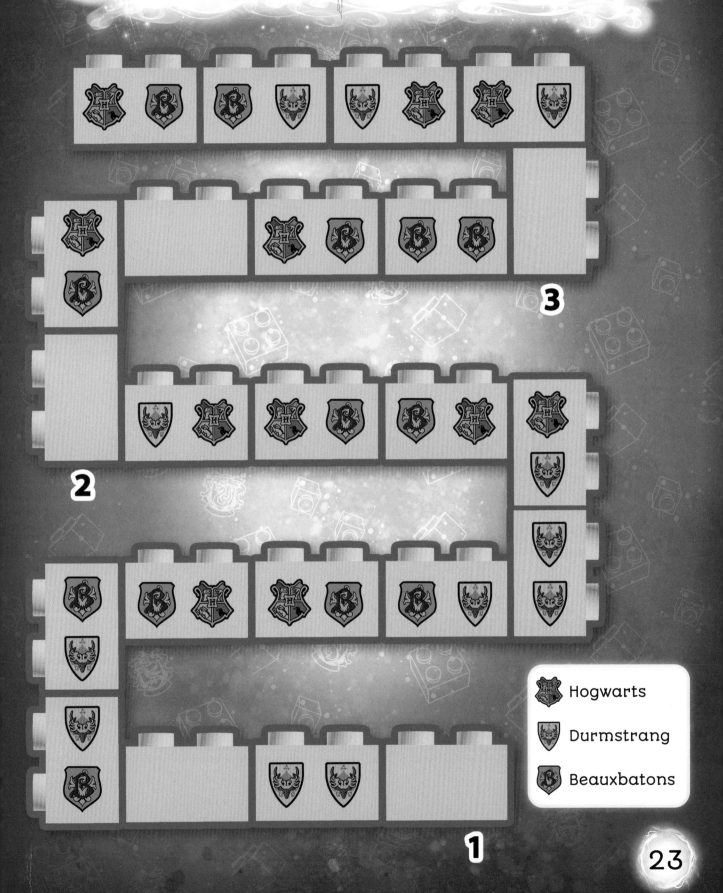

Hogwarts	
Durmstrang	
Beauxbatons	

SOME GAME!

Use the stickers to finish the Triwizard Maze, then put the competitors in the correct order at the starting line.

- Harry comes first.
- Viktor comes second.
- Fleur comes last.
- Cedric enters with Harry.

3

2

1

START

Now go through the maze with the young wizards.

FINISH

THE FINAL ENCOUNTER

Has another player joined the Tournament?
Perhaps not ... Place the stickers to reveal who
Harry's opponent is.

TOM RIDDLE

26

THE TWIN CORES

When Harry and Voldemort's wands connected, something unusual happened. Place the stickers on the letters the arrows point to and find out what.

G P R A I S

R O R S I K

I P T N O C

G A R N T A

T R E G M E

ANSWER:

....

....

27

A SNEAKY TEACHER

Stick in the missing portraits and follow the arrows to find out who turned the winner's cup into a Portkey!

START

SEE YOU SOON!

The Tournament is over. Complete the frames with stickers and find the fragments that do not belong in the picture.

Answers

p. 1

p. 2

p. 3

FLEUR DELACOUR   CEDRIC DIGGORY

VIKTOR KRUM   HARRY POTTER

p. 4

p. 5

p. 6

p. 7

1 Swedish Short-Snout   3 Hungarian Horntail

2 Common Welsh Green   4 Chinese Fireball

1   3   2   4

pp. 8–9

p. 10
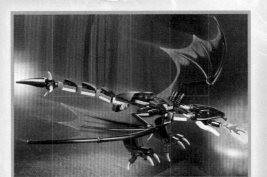

p. 11

p. 12
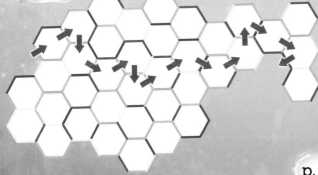

p. 13

sample answer

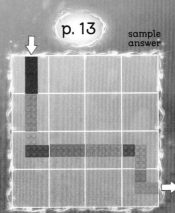

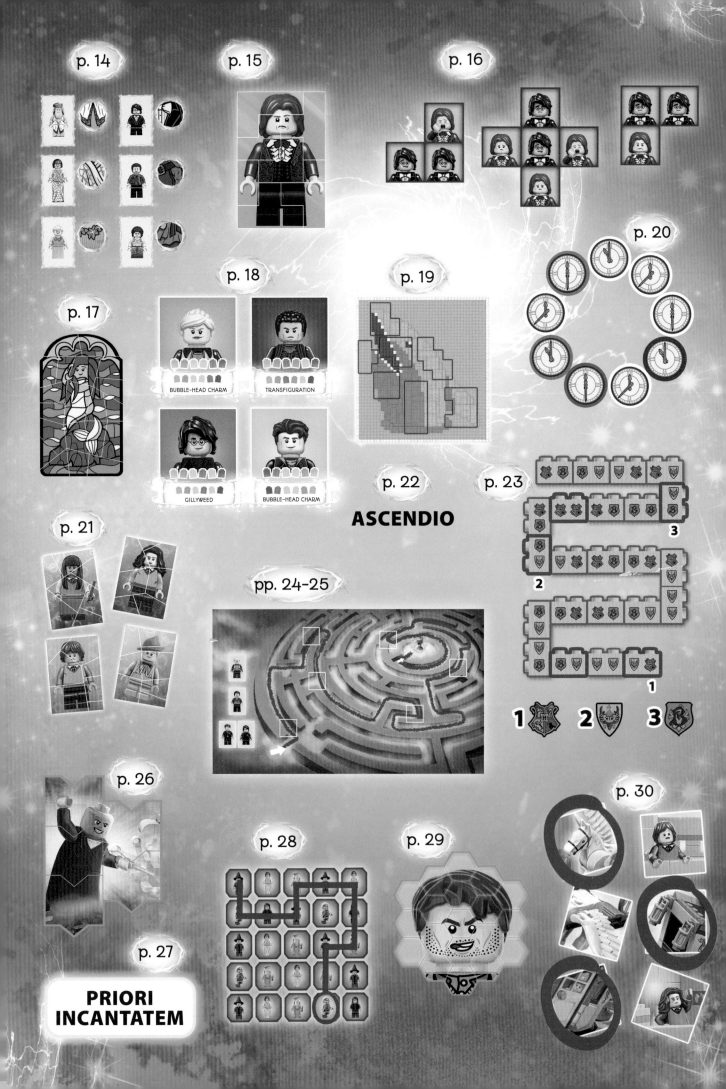

p. 14

p. 15

p. 16

p. 17

p. 18

BUBBLE-HEAD CHARM

TRANSFIGURATION

GILLYWEED

BUBBLE-HEAD CHARM

p. 19

p. 20

p. 21

p. 22

ASCENDIO

p. 23

1

2

3

1

2

3

pp. 24-25

p. 26

p. 27

PRIORI INCANTATEM

p. 28

p. 29

p. 30